Collins

School Journey to the Centre of the Earth

by

Daisy Campbell

with

Ken Campbell

Resource Material by
Suzi Graham-Adriani
and
Anthony Banks

William Collins' dream of knowledge for all began with the publication of his first book in 1819. A self-educated mill worker, he not only enriched millions of lives, but also founded a flourishing publishing house. Today, staying true to this spirit, Collins books are packed with inspiration, innovation and a practical expertise. They place you at the centre of a world of possibility and give you exactly what you need to explore it.

Collins. Do more.

Published by Collins
An imprint of HarperCollins*Publishers*
77–85 Fulham Palace Road
Hammersmith
London
W6 8JB

Commissioned by Charlie Evans
Design by JPD
Cover design by Charlotte Wilkinson
Production by Katie Butler
Printed and bound by Imago

Browse the complete Collins catalogue at www.collinseducation.com

British Library Cataloguing in Publication Data

A Catalogue record for this publication is available from the British Library

Acknowledgements

Photo credits: p70, 73 and 75, Gemma Mount; p77 The Ronald Grant Archive; p78 Empics; p80 The Ronald Grant Archive.

Text credits: p84–5, extract from *Just William* by Richmal Crompton is reproduced with permission of MacMillan Children's Books; extract from *The Lion, the Witch and the Wardrobe* is reprinted with permission of HarperCollins Publishers Ltd © C.S. Lewis Pte Limited 1950.

Contents

Characters

The children of class 4S:

THE GIRLS

STACEY eight and three quarters

BEE nine next Tuesday

CHRISSY same as Stacey

MIRACLE nine

ANNA nine in twenty one days

TRICIA eight and three quarters and a bit

JENELLE nine this week

THE BOYS

SONNY eight and a quarter

RAB nine last week

JAMES just nine

SAM unknown

BEN eight and a half

TOM ten in three weeks

MATTHEW nearly nine

MISS SHEEHAN Class teacher of 4S

School Journey to the Centre of the Earth

The morning of the class 4S school trip to Alton Towers. Beside the coach there is general chaos, with children singing, skipping, fighting, dancing, screaming etc.

STACEY   That ain't fair, Bee. You promised me three weeks ago that I could sit next to you on the coach.

BEE   Yeah, but I promised Chrissy four weeks ago.

STACEY   *(storming off)* That ain't fair. I'm telling Miss.

CHRISSY   Whatever. *(to **Miracle**)* See EastEnders yesterday?

MIRACLE   *(defensive)* Yeah.

CHRISSY   I can't believe we're gonna miss it today. What do you reckon Alfie's gonna say to Kat?

MIRACLE   Umm, well, what is it again? She's doing sex with the...

CHRISSY   No no no no. She's not doing sex...

BEE   *(butting in)* Ohmigod, what about Sonia's little girl? She's gonna get run over.

ANNA   Ohmigod!

MIRACLE   Hey, maybe there's tellies at Alton Towers.

RAB   *(butting in)* Or we could arrange for the driver to run over a baby on the way, then it'll be like bringing EastEnders right to yer doorstep!

JAMES	Rah that's bare good, Rab.

He does an elaborate impression, with sound effects, of a baby getting run over: Waah waah – splat – crunch etc.

ANNA	That's not even funny. Babies have feelings, you know. It's not like in EastEnders where it's made up. They don't really kill the baby in EastEnders, you know. It's made up.
RAB	*(doing a 'der-brain' impression)* No! Is it really?
TRICIA	Oh, Sonny! I thought you weren't gonna make it!
SONNY	My mum had another party last night. I only got her into bed at, like, past midnight.
JENELLE	*(To **Tricia**)* I'm having the window seat.
TRICIA	I don't fink so.
JENELLE	*(doing hip head-wagging à la Jerry Springer)* Girlfriend, put it like this: I don't get the window seat, you don't get to sit next to me. Oh hi, Sonny.
SONNY	*(to **Tricia**)* Is Jenelle sitting with us?
TRICIA	Yep.
SONNY	Can I tell you a huge secret? No, forget it.
TRICIA	Sonny, you're my best friend. I tell you all my secrets.
SONNY	Do best-friend shake on it.

They do an elaborate handshake.

SONNY	You promise you'll never tell?

TRICIA	Cross my heart and hope to die, stick a needle in my eye.

Sonny whispers in Tricia's ear. Her eyes widen at the juiciness of the secret. A large crowd of boys burst suddenly through them, screaming.

THE BOYS	Back of the bus! Back of the bus!

*On hearing this, all the kids make a wild dash for the back of the coach. They eventually all find seats inside. All heads are now on the same level, popping up when their names are called from the register. They continue talking over **Miss Sheehan**'s attempts to take the register.*

MISS SHEEHAN	Right, settle down. Rab? Stop. James! Enough. OK, Tricia – stop talking, please. Rab. That's enough. SHUT UP! Thank you. Right. Sonny?
SONNY	Yes, Miss Sheehan.
MISS SHEEHAN	Anna?
ANNA	Yes, Miss Sheehan.
MISS SHEEHAN	James?

Pause.

TRICIA	*(doing a 'der-brain' impression)* James!
JAMES	What? Oh, yes, Miss.
MISS SHEEHAN	What did you miss?
JAMES	What? Oh, yes, Miss Sheehan.
MISS SHEEHAN	Miracle.
MIRACLE	Yes, Miss Sheehan
MISS SHEEHAN	Jenelle?

JENELLE	Arsenal beat Tottenham two-nil.
MISS SHEEHAN	And what a game it was. Rab?
RAB	Here, Miss Sheehan.
MISS SHEEHAN	Sam.
SAM	*(loudly)* Yes, Miss Sheehan!
MISS SHEEHAN	Tricia?
TRICIA	*(even louder)* Yes, Miss Sheehan.

It is now apparent that this is a game. The one who can answer in the loudest voice wins.

MISS SHEEHAN	Chrissy?
CHRISSY	*(louder)* Here, Miss.
MISS SHEEHAN	Stacey.
STACEY	*(louder)* Yes, Miss!
MISS SHEEHAN	Bee?
BEE	*(almost screaming)* Yes, Miss!
MISS SHEEHAN	Ben?
BEN	*(at normal volume)* I am present, Miss Sheehan.
EVERYONE	*(doing elaborate 'der-brain' impressions)* Mr Bean! Mr Bean!

Tom, a small-sized boy, gets on the coach and looks for a space. Despite the abundance of free seats, they all appear to be saved.

RAB	*(seeing Tom)* Tramp! Incoming, lads.
JAMES	You're late, Tom. You Michael Jackson wannabee.

The register is still going on in the background.

MATTHEW   *(as **Tom** attempts to sit down)* Sorry, saved.

CHRISSY   Sorry, saved.

STACEY   Sorry, saved.

Many are still waving goodbye to their parents through the window, but are beginning to tire of this activity and are chatting to friends at the same time.

RAB   Sorry. This is a Clark's-shoe-free zone.

MISS SHEEHAN   Rab, let Tom sit there, please.

TOM   Thank you, Miss. *(he sits)*

RAB   Miss, I'm charging you with the doctor's bill when we all catch lurgy.

JAMES   *(to **Rab**)* Jexies!

Rab and James touch their heads, then cross their arms to touch their shoulders then touch their waists.

EVERYONE   Lurgies ejected for life!

MISS SHEEHAN   OK, has everyone got their sick bags?

EVERYONE   *(holding up see-through plastic bags)* Yes, Miss.

BEE   Can't we get the paper sort, Miss? These sort are disgustin'. If anyone's sick you can see right through them.

STACEY   The paper ones are worse, though. If you're sick in those, they go all soggy at the bottom and burst.

BEE   Thanks for that, Stace.

ANNA	Oh. Miss. I've left my pack-lunch box in the classroom. Can I go and get it?
JAMES	No, you can starve.
MISS SHEEHAN	Quickly.
ANNA	Thanks, Miss.

*She runs off the coach. The electronic sound of a GameBoy becomes audible. It is traced to **Chrissy**. Everyone in the surrounding seats leans in, intent on seeing how badly she's doing.*

SAM	*('der-brain' impression)* No! You've got to go down under that path and switch the lever, then you can get over the bridge. No! Only puss-in-boots can climb that wall!
STACEY	*(sarcastically)* You don't say.
SAM	Jump! Jump! Ah. You missed it.
STACEY	It ain't fair. I'm feelin' carsick.
TOM	We haven't even set off yet.

*Every time **Tom** speaks he is mocked.*

BEN	By my calculation we should have left fifteen minutes ago…
RAB	Quiet, everyone. He speaks. Mr Bean has something he wishes to share. What was it? Mr Bean?
BEN	*(while **Rab** impersonates him behind his back)* According to my watch, the accuracy of which is governed by satellite, we should have begun our journey fifteen minutes, twelve seconds and… thirty-two milliseconds ago…

EVERYONE	Shut up, Mr Bean!

Anna has returned with her lunch box. She goes quickly back to her seat. The coach revs up, and from the movement of the children and their frantic waving out of the back window, it is obvious that their journey has begun. Tricia is still waving frantically out of the back window. Sonny and Jenelle sit on either side of her.

TRICIA	Bye, Mum. Mummy... *(crying)* I'm homesick.
JENELLE	Shaaaame! Tricia's crying!
TRICIA	I'm not cryin', I'm not. Anyway, don't vex me. You're not in the gang. Me and Sonny are a gang and we're well nang. We're the Nang Gang.

Sonny and Tricia do their elaborate handshake.

JENELLE	You fink I wanna be in your neeky gang?
TRICIA	Yeah, well we've got gang secrets. We tell each other everything. Everything. You wouldn't believe some of the stuff Sonny's told me.

Tricia suddenly appears far more pally with Jenelle than with Sonny. Sonny looks left out. He grabs Tricia's arm.

JENELLE	Like what?
SONNY	You say anything, I'll never speak to you ever again.
JENELLE	What sort of secrets 'as he told you?
TRICIA	I'm sworn to secrecy.
JENELLE	Yeah, obviously. What are they?

SONNY	I'll break your neck!
TRICIA	Well. Don't say that I told you, but Sonny well fancies you.
SONNY	*(suddenly sitting back in his seat)* That's not... you said... you weren't gonna... anyway, it's not true, anyway.
TRICIA	You love her.
SONNY	I don't. In fact, I hate her, see? *(he pulls a disgusting face at **Jenelle**)*
TRICIA	*(singing)* Sonny and Jenelle up a tree. K-I-S-S-I-N-G!
SONNY	Look! You're the most smelly *(mouthing the word)* bitch I ever saw. *(proudly, to **Tricia**)* See?
TRICIA	Hold hands! Hold hands!
SONNY	I hate her! Look! *(he hits **Jenelle**)*
JENELLE	OW!
TRICIA	You two are gonna get married.
JENELLE	I don't fink so.
SONNY	I'm never talkin' to you ever again.
TRICIA	Oh, Sonny. You're my best friend.
JAMES	*(popping up)* Oi, do you wanna hear the sickest thing ever?
TRICIA	James! This is an AB conversation. C your way out of it.
JAMES	*(making letter symbols with his fingers: M W M)* Your Mum Works in McDonald's.
TRICIA	You think you're so nang.

JAMES	Yep.
TRICIA	Well, you're not. *(shouting)* Hands up who thinks James is nang.

*Rab shoots his hand up. After a glare from **James**, so does **Sonny**. **Jenelle** has her hand sort of halfway. **James** doesn't even look to see who's on his side.*

TRICIA	See? Three.
JAMES	No one else heard you. And anyway, I'm not gonna even ask anyone what they think of you, 'cos you'd be so upset that you'd throw yourself off the coach. And you're so fat that you'd go right through the world and come out at Australia.
TRICIA	No.
JAMES	You would.
TRICIA	Wouldn't.
JAMES	Would.
BEN	Actually, she wouldn't.
TRICIA	Thanks, Mr Bean.
BEN	Yes, even weighing 950 thousand, billion, zillion tonnes…
TRICIA	*(hits **Ben**)* Thanks a lot.
BEN	No no. Just supposing. Well, even then, due to gravity, the furthest Tricia could possibly fall would be to the centre of the earth.
TRICIA	Yeah. Well, it's great down there. I've been.
JAMES	That's a lie.

BEE	Yeah, what's it like, then?
TRICIA	Well, you go down this tunnel in Staffordshire…
ANNA	That's where we're going, isn't it?
TRICIA	Yeah, see, I'm not actually supposed to tell you this, but we're not actually going to Alton Towers at all.
ANNA	What?
TRICIA	We are actually going to the centre of the earth.
BEE	*(sarcastically)* Yeah, right.

Bee, James, Anna, Ben try and shout Tricia down.

TRICIA	No, it's true. Ask my granny. Ask my turtle. We're on a mission but we don't know it.
EVERYONE	Eh?
TRICIA	At least, you lot don't know it.
EVERYONE	Eh?
TRICIA	What I'm gonna tell is very dangerous information.
EVERYONE	Eh?
TRICIA	In fact, it's probably best that I don't tell.
ANNA	No, tell.
TRICIA	No, Anna. It's too dangerous for you to know.
EVERYONE	*(disappointed)* Oo-oh.
TRICIA	So, you two. When's the wedding?

JENELLE	Shut up. Anyway, Simon might get jealous.
TRICIA	Who's Simon?
SONNY	The pieman.

*Sarcastic laughs from **Tricia** and **Jenelle** at **Sonny**'s unsuccessful joke.*

JENELLE	You bricked it, butter breath.
TRICIA	That's so sad. So who is Simon?
JENELLE	He's my boyfriend. He's thirteen.
TRICIA & SONNY	THIRTEEN?!
SONNY	Older boys are stupid.
JENELLE	Older boys are the best.
TRICIA	That's like your dad, though!
SONNY	They only want you for one thing.
JENELLE	What do they want me for?
SONNY	Well. They only want you for one thing. Like, that thing could be anything, but, thing is, they only want you for that and not for nothing else. My uncle's older than my aunt and she said that's true. I reckon it's her cooking.
TRICIA	She good?
SONNY	Yeah, she made this bare yummy ice-cream cake for my eighth birthday. But she is fat. Like, really, really fat. She's one of those people you can't imagine on the loo.
TRICIA	Yeah, 'cos like if she sat on the loo, all her flab would bulge over the edges and touch the floor either side.

JENELLE	Gross! You two are so immature.
SONNY	Just 'cos you've got an older boyfriend.
TRICIA	I am eight and three-quarters and I am almost nine.
JENELLE	I'm nine this week.
TRICIA	Well, I'm nine last week. I'm eleven. I'm fifteen. I'm seventeen. I work in Sue Ryder. I'm married.
JENELLE	Shut…
TRICIA	I am married.
JENELLE	To who?
SONNY	Michael Jackson.
JENELLE	Urghh…
TRICIA	No. Robbie.
JENELLE	What, so you're Mrs Williams?
TRICIA	Yeah.
JENELLE	But you're not. Oh deeeee-aaaar. You got slewed!
TRICIA	I am.
JENELLE	No. You're Tricia Park. Which means you lied. Liar, liar. Pants on fire.
TRICIA	No, but you see, 'cos you're not s'posed to get married until you're grown-up, I have to have a fake name; 'cos I've got married before I should, and if the police found out they'd hang me.
SONNY	Don't be stupid. They don't have the death penalty any more.

TRICIA	Yeah, they do. But only for treason and getting married to pop stars when you're too young.
SONNY	What's treason?
TRICIA	It's cussing down the Royal Family.
JENELLE	Sonny, do you really think I'm buff?
SONNY	Yeah!
TRICIA	*(very loudly)* Woah! Everyone! Sonny's telling Jenelle that he loves her.
EVERYONE	*(getting higher and higher pitched)* Oooooooooooooooooooooo!
SONNY	No, I never.
JENELLE	You said I was buff.
SONNY	Exactly.
TRICIA	Sonny, do you actually know what 'buff' means?
SONNY	Yeah.

Sonny becomes aware that everyone is listening in.

TRICIA	What, then?
SONNY	*(suddenly unsure)* It's like a mixture between *(mouthing the words)* bitch and guff.

*Everyone does elaborate 'der-brain' impressions. **Sonny** is mortified.*

JAMES	*(hidden behind his seat)* Who let off a smelly one? Come on, own the stinker. Who ate egg this morning?

CHRISSY	Anyway, you fancy the driver.

Stacey looks at the driver then sticks her fingers down her throat.

STACEY	That's disgusting. He is butters. And he stinks.
CHRISSY	Perfect match, then. You told me the other day that you wet the bed and that your mum got well angry with you.
RAB	*(popping up)* Rah. She got yer. Boyage! You got slewed!
JAMES & RAB	*(right in her face)* How-do-you-feel?
JAMES	What happened?
RAB	She wets the bed.
JAMES	Oh, tramp! You live in a cardboard box.
STACEY	I didn't. That's not… It wasn't me.
JAMES	It wasn't you? What, someone's been crawlin' into your bed at night, pissin' and then crawlin' out again?
STACEY	I spilled a glass of water, alright.

Sarcastic, sympathetic nods, and chin scratching.

CHRISSY	An' I feel sorry for your sister who has to sleep in the same bed.
JAMES & RAB	Urghh.
STACEY	That is a lie. My sister… I haven't got a sister.
CHRISSY	Yes you do.

STACEY	Alright. But she doesn't sleep in the same bed. We've got bunk beds, and I get the top one 'cos I'm good.
RAB	So it must drip through.
CHRISSY	Urrrgh.
STACEY	I don't wet the bed. I don't wet the bed. I'm not listening. *(putting her hands over her ears)* Din din din. I'm not listening.
RAB	I wouldn't sleep with you.

Pause.

	I mean, in a bed.
STACEY	I'm going to the toilet.

*She sticks two fingers up at **Sonny**, who does the same to her.*

RAB	Yeah, we wouldn't want you doin' it on your seat.
JAMES	P'raps you should sleep on the bog. That would solve all your problems.
BEN	The turbulence is interfering with my digestive tract. By the time we get there I'll be too sick to go on the any of the big rides.
SAM	Have you been on the big one at Alton Towers?
MIRACLE	The Corkscrew! I've been on that one! It's wicked, innit?
SAM	Yeah, I've been on that, like, ten times. I love that bit, you know, when you're slowly goin' up and then…

TOM	Oh yeah, an' then you, like, wait at the top for, like, ages…
SAM	It's only a couple of seconds…
TOM	Yeah, but it feels like…
SAM	Yeah, it feels like ages, and then suddenly it dips…

Everyone screams.

SONNY	Yeah, an' your tummy gets left behind.
SAM	Yeah, your tummy. An' then before you know it you're goin'…

They have begun to live the ride. One by one, the others join in, swerving and lurching in formation.

MIRACLE	On the upside-down bit…
TOM	An' you're 'Waaaah!' and 'Ooooo!'
JENELLE	An' then you turn the corner an'…
MIRACLE	You think you're gonna come off the rails and 'Weeeee!' and 'Aaaaaargh!'

They scream and shout over the top of each other:

JENELLE	Woooh!
MATTHEW	Aaaaah!
SONNY	Excelleeeent!
SAM	Heeeelp!

etc.

BEN	And then it's the end of the ride.
EVERYONE	Shut up, Mr Bean.
MIRACLE	We haven't got to the best bit yet.
MATTHEW	So you start to climb up again…

Everyone is leaning back as they climb the second loop. Then they hang at the top and bomb down.

SONNY	An' now we're right upside down…
JENELLE	An' we stop for a couple of seconds…
SAM	Yeah, you stop right upside down…

The children all appear to be hanging upside down. Suddenly there is a complete silence: a long pause while they hang.

MIRACLE	And then…

Everyone lurches forward and hurtles down the second loop, a look of terror on their faces. They scream and shout over the top of each other:

SONNY	Help!
TOM	I want to get off!
SAM	Wicked!
SONNY	Can I open my eyes yet?
JENELLE	I'm gonna die! I'm gonna die!
MATTHEW	I hate it! I hate it!

etc.

MIRACLE	An' we're goin' round the corner…

They lurch to the side as they go round a sharp bend.

> An' we're comin' to the end...

They are all thrown forward as the ride stops. They pant heavily.

> What do you think?

TOM	*(breathless)* That's excellent.
STACEY	*(returning from the toilet)* Out.
JAMES	Talk about take yer time on the bog. That bog's for everyone, you know. Not just for people with bladder problems.
STACEY	Get out of my seat.
JAMES	Urrrgh. Yours is it? I thought it was a bit damp.
STACEY	If you ain't careful I'll wee on you.
JAMES	Wow. You've been on the bog all that time and you've still got enough left to wee on me? You're amazing, Stace. I gotta say. You're world-class pisser of the year.
ANNA	Please tell me what's going on, Tricia.
TRICIA	*(super-fast)* Oh, well Sonny said Jenelle was buff, and I told them about how I'm married to Robbie, then someone guffed, then Stacey said she fancies the driver who smells of wee and then she wet her seat...
ANNA	No, the secret mission. The centre of the earth.
TRICIA	Oh, that. *(pause)* Well, I suppose if I tell you what's going on you might be more prepared. We're being kidnapped for... A super top-secret, mega-scary mission. They're going to watch us to see if we can live down there.

ANNA	They?
TRICIA	*(whispering)* Terrorists.
ANNA	Terrorists?
TRICIA	Very dangerous men.
BEE	And women!
TRICIA	Bee! I wasn't gonna mention the women.
ANNA	Worse than the men?
TRICIA	Much. I wish Bee had kept her mouth shut. I didn't want to frighten you.
ANNA	Well, what are these women like? How can they be so terrible?
TRICIA	You know Pat Butcher off EastEnders? They all look like her. They're not really humans. They're, sort of, robots. They're programmed to kill. They've all got really long, sharp red nails like Pat's. If you was to clean out their nails, you'd find dried-up flesh and blood under 'em, from where they'd scraped off little children's faces.

Horrified, **Anna** tentatively touches her face.

TRICIA	The men give the orders. The women are just, sort of like, killing machines. The Butcher-bots.
ANNA & BEE	No!
TRICIA	It's an experiment. An evil plot.
BEE	They wouldn't pick us. They'd want people who were properly trained.
TRICIA	No, that's the whole point. They've got to put down people who don't know anything about

the experiment. People who aren't gonna grass them up – school children. It's obvious. People they can 'nipulate.

ANNA   You mean we're goin' down there for the rest of our lives?

TRICIA   Yeah. Why'd you think I got homesick at the beginning? D'you think I'd get homesick if I was just going to Alton Towers for the weekend? No, of course I wouldn't. But for the rest of my life…

ANNA   But I didn't even say goodbye to my mum. I just told her not to forget to record EastEnders.

TRICIA   Ah, well. It's too late now. And you're gonna miss EastEnders for the rest of your life.

BEE   Doesn't matter, anyway. It's ending soon.

ANNA   Isn't there any way of stopping it?

BEE   No, they're gonna blow up Albert Square and that'll be the end…

ANNA   No, I mean, going to the centre of the earth.

TRICIA   'Fraid not.

ANNA   Well, shouldn't we tell Miss Sheehan?

TRICIA   She's in on it. So's the coach driver. There's no hope, I'm afraid.

ANNA   Miss!

TRICIA   You could ask her. But she's gonna deny it, 'cos they're not gonna tell us until there's no way out. They can't take the risk.

ANNA   MISS!

TRICIA	Miss Sheehan's a terrorist. *(pause)* She's trying to find out about the centre of the earth for Bin Laden, so they can burrow underneath and set up camp there and then spring up from the sewers when we're least expecting it and kill us all and take over the world.
ANNA	But Miss Sheehan always seemed so nice.
TRICIA	I know. I'm sorry you had to learn this way.
BEE	But wait a minute. Miss Sheehan supports Arsenal.
TRICIA	All part of the cunning disguise.
ANNA	How do you know all this?
TRICIA	Well, it makes sense, doesn't it?
RAB	You've been watchin' way too many movies, Trish.
JAMES	Yeah, those 'U's that you've been watching 'ave gone straight to your head.
RAB	Yeah, like – Tweenies' and the Teletubbies' big day out!

Rab and James do impressions of Tweenies and Teletubbies.

TOM	*(urgently)* I heard Mr Harris and Miss Sheehan talking…
RAB	Urggggh, Tom, don't come near me with those shoes!
JAMES	That's deep.
RAB	No, listen, they went out when the dinosaurs came in!

JAMES	That's sad.
RAB	Yeah, I know. But I just said it to keep in with Tom.
JAMES	Oh you're a joker, bruv. Oh dear, Tom.
RAB & JAMES	How-do-you-feel?
RAB	Arrrgh. You gonna beat me up, Tom? No, Tom, please don't beat me up. I'll have to go and find Mumsy.
JAMES	Where does your mum shop, Tom? Oxfam?
RAB	No, Ultra Oxfam! Tom. Did you know?
JAMES	Did you know? Did you know?
RAB	That cats lay eggs. That's true actually, please.
TOM	No, they don't.
RAB	Yes they do 'cos my dad told me, actually.
JAMES	An' his dad's a scientist.
RAB	Did you know that?
TOM	Yeah.

Rab and James find this answer hysterically funny.

TOM	*(desperately)* They don't lay eggs. I meant about his dad. They don't lay eggs. I meant I knew his dad's a scientist.
RAB	Vexed. You got slewed.
JAMES	'at was wicked. 'at was wicked.
TOM	They don't lay eggs. I know they don't.

RAB	Aw, what a nice Winnie the Pooh lunch box, Tom. Was it part of the Oxfam summer sale? Ultra mega Oxfam summer sale? Ultra mega Oxfamopolis.
TOM	Please listen! Please listen!
BEE	Rab! Let him speak.
RAB	Shup, Bee, his mum's a Teletubbie.
BEE	Let him speak.
RAB	*(mimicking)* Let him speak.
TOM	I heard him and Miss Sheehan talking.
BEE	What were they saying?
TOM	That the school journey might not go quite as planned, and that, knowing us, we'd all end up lost.
TRICIA	How did they look?
TOM	I don't know. Kind of shifty.
TRICIA	Mmmm. They were talking in code.
BEE	Mr Harris is one of them?
TRICIA	All the teachers are. Those meetings they have. They're all to plan how they're gonna capture us. It was Mr Harris's idea. He's a nasty piece of work is Harris. His wife's one of those 'Pat robots'.
BEE & ANNA	Not a Butcher-bot?
MIRACLE	I've met her. She's nothing like that.
TRICIA	Obviously not to meet people. By day she's a nice, kind old lady. By night it's all a bit more sinister.

MIRACLE	I met her at 8.30 in the evening.
TRICIA	You were lucky, then. The change happens at 9.00. Half an hour more and you'd have no face.
MIRACLE	*(amazed)* Now I think about it she did suddenly run off at about ten to nine. Some meeting or something.
BEE	Really?
MIRACLE	Yes.
BEE	That is spooky.
MIRACLE	But I still don't understand how come you know all about these terrorists.
TRICIA	Ah, well, my dear Miracle. That's a bit more cleverer. For a start, Sheehankov is a known terrorist name, but to fool us all she's cunningly missed off the 'kov' bit. And also purple is the terrorists' special colour code, and, as we all know, purple is Miss Sheehan or should I say Miss Sheehankov's favourite colour.

*They look in astonishment at **Miss Sheehan**(kov).*

TOM	*(tentatively)* What does the purple code mean?
TRICIA	It means 'kill the children'. Depending on what colour they're wearing, the chiefs can tell what kind of terrorist department they work for.
SAM	You can tell they're terrorists by the colour of their skin. Miss Sheehan isn't dark.
MIRACLE	That's rubbish, Sam. Terrorists can have any colour skin. My mum says so. She says that the worst kind are the ones that pretend to be good people who have smiley families and nice suits

	and all that, and are secretly selling people bombs.
SAM	Yeah, well, my mum said that if dark people weren't allowed to come into the country it would never have happened.
MIRACLE	Yeah, but everyone knows your mum's a racialist.
SAM	No, she's not. She just says we got enough of them now.
MIRACLE	That is so wrong, Sam. If I tell Miss Sheehan that you're a racialist you'll be in big trouble. Miss!
SAM	No, don't! Miss Sheehan's a terrorist.
TOM	But I thought terrorists live in cyberspace.
TRICIA	Yeah, and where do you think cyberspace is?
EVERYONE	Where?

Tricia points down. The others all look down.

| TRICIA | The terrorists are just a front… |
| EVERYONE | For what? |

Pause.

TRICIA	That ain't the point. Point is we're on a school journey to the centre of the earth.
RAB	*(popping up)* Cack. Cack. The liar needs a slap.
SAM	*(spotting a Mini out the window)* Mini Cooper! No returns.

He punches **STACEY**. *She punches him back.*

STACEY	Mini Cooper!
SAM	Oi, you can't do that! I said no returns.
STACEY	No you never.
ANNA	Yeah he did, Stacey.
SONNY	Umm. You get a free slap for that, Sam.
STACEY	No! That ain't fair.
RAB	It's the law, Stace. We can't make exceptions, can we, Sonny?
SONNY	No. Put out your hand, Stace.
STACEY	No! Please don't!
EVERYONE	*(getting higher and higher pitched)* Oooooooooooooooo!

Sam *slaps* **Stacey**'s *hand hard. She bursts into tears.*

JAMES	Shut up, Stacey. You better be tougher than that when the terrorists come for us.
JENELLE	*(popping up)* What's this?
BEE	Trish reckons we're goin' to the centre of the earth, wiv purple spies or something.
SONNY	Oh yeah, I wonder what the Arabesques are a front for?
BEN	*(popping up)* You're getting it all muddled. The Arab culture is ancient and fascinating –
RAB, JENELLE, ANNA, JAMES	Shut up, Mr Bean!

BEN	They invented the alphabet...
EVERYONE	Shut up, Mr Bean!
JENELLE	Nah, he's right. It's not the Arabesques. It's the Funny Mentalists.
STACEY	It's the North Koreans what are really behind it all.
TRICIA	Ahh, Stacey. I would never have guessed.
STACEY	Guessed what?
TRICIA	That it was you. I was told someone would be sent to give me vital information. Thank you.
STACEY	*(confused, but pleased with the attention)* Oh that's alright. I mean, think nothing of it... Comrade.
JENELLE	Right, so let's look at the facts.
TOM	There are no facts. Only guesses.
TRICIA	You shut up. How old are you?
TOM	*(smugly)* Ten in three weeks. How old are you?
TRICIA	Yeah, well that don't matter. A few months don't make no difference to anyone. Anyway, clever arse, where do you think all the terrorists are hiding and making the MWD?
TOM	It is too hot for anything to live down there. Science says so.
TRICIA	I don't know what scientists you've been chattin' with, but the one I've spoken to lives down there. So, so much for all your 'science says so' crap.

*She sticks her tongue out at **Tom**.*

RAB	Murked, boy. That was jokes, Trish. Pity you were talkin' outta your bum.

*Everyone laughs at **Tricia**. **Rab** and **James** slap hands.*

TRICIA	Fine. When you get down there you'll be sorry. You'll wish you listened to your dear old mate, Trish, when you're trapped by evil terrorists, poking you with needles and pulling your hair out and...
RAB	Who's seen War of the Worlds?
MIRACLE	Yeah. It's bare good!
JAMES	I thought it was crap.
MIRACLE	Yeah, I s'pose it wasn't that good.
RAB	What's your favourite bit?
MIRACLE	Oh, erm... I saw it ages ago, so... Erm... I can't really remember.
JAMES	It's only just come out.
MIRACLE	*(desperate)* Oh. Maybe I'm getting it muddled up with another film....
RAB	Which other film?
MIRACLE	I don't know what it's called. I saw it ages ago.
JAMES	So you haven't actually seen War of the Worlds?
MIRACLE	Erm... No. I don't think I have. I got muddled.
RAB	Do you like the bit when the aliens come?
MIRACLE	I told you. I haven't seen it.
RAB	No, but that bit's on the trailer. You must've seen it on TV.

MIRACLE	Oh, yeah. 'Course. *(quickly changing the subject)* So, Trish, tell us more about the terrorists.
STACEY	How do you get down to the centre of the earth? I mean, how would you, supposin' we was goin', which I don't believe anyway.
TRICIA	Ah, well. That's the cunning bit.
JAMES	Whoever nicked my Twix had best give it back, unless they wanna die a slow and painful death.
JENELLE	Vex up! Stress monkey! Watch it, everyone. James might turn nasty.
TRICIA	You know the roller coaster at Alton Towers?
MIRACLE	Yeah. The Corkscrew.
RAB	Yeah, it's wicked, man.
JENELLE	Yeah, that bit when it dips down is blindin'.

Everyone does roller coaster noises.

CHRISSY	Yeah, and then you start goin' up slowly…
RAB	And then you get to the top bit…

They are all set to take another ride on their imaginary roller coaster.

TRICIA	No, not that one. You know the one in the dark? The underground one?
CHRISSY	Oh, The Blackhole?

They get ready to go down The Blackhole.

TRICIA	Yeah, whatever. Miss Sheehankov will give…

MATTHEW	Sheehankov?
JENELLE	It's Miss Sheehan's secret Funny Mentalist name.
MATTHEW	Oh, right.
TRICIA	Yeah, well she'll give the signal when the train's filled up with us lot, and the man what works The Blackhole will switch the tracks so instead of goin' back to the beginning, the ground opens up and we go plummeting down into the centre of the earth.

They all go down the Blackhole.

JAMES	Rah, that's sick, man.
MIRACLE	Yeah, like the longest roller coaster ever... Straight down...
JAMES	Mad.
TOM	Wow. Those terrorists are clever.
JENELLE	Yeah.
ANNA	But our parents will notice we've gone.
TRICIA	For a while, yeah. But you know all these kids that vanish, like when they're skiing and stuff?
MIRACLE	Yeah?
TRICIA	That's where they've gone. We'll probably see them down there.
MATTHEW	They died, didn't they?
TRICIA	That's what everyone was told. But it's all part of The Spirisy.

36

ANNA	The Spirisy?
TRICIA	That's what it is. The Spirisy.
ANNA	What's the Spirisy?
TRICIA	You know, like Diana.
CHRISSY	Who's Diana?
TRICIA	You know, the princess who was killed by the Queen. That was the beginning of The Spirisy. The Queen wanted Diana to marry her son but Diana wanted to marry Saddam Bin Laden, so the Queen poisoned Diana's driver…
MATTHEW	Oh, is that why he knocked down the Twin Towers?
TRICIA	Yes, because Diana had twins in her tummy when she was killed by the Queen, so Saddam knocked down the Twin Towers to get revenge, then Prime Minister Bush smashed up the Arabists, because he's in love with the Queen, who's actually a lizard. That's The Spirisy.
SONNY	Oh, is this to do with the Nasties?
TRICIA	Be careful, Sonny. You're closer to the truth than you know.
JAMES	The Nasties?
SONNY	You know the ones who burned loads of people in chimneys and gave out gold stars.
JAMES	Oh yeah, they're cool.
BEN	You know there is a theory that the Nazis…
EVERYONE	Shut up, Mr Bean!
SONNY	No, I want to hear this.

BEN	There is a theory that the Nazis were simply one incarnation of a much more ancient and secretive cult, that has emerged throughout the ages to perform genocides.
RAB	What is he talkin' about?
BEN	Apparently, a large amount of energy is released during mass murder, and if you know the technique you can absorb it and become instantly immortal. That's what the Nazis were trying to do…
SONNY	What, so the Nasties never actually went away? We never actually beat them at war?
TRICIA	No, they just went underground.
JAMES	What, so the Nasties are running The Spirisy from under the ground?
TRICIA	What have I been trying to tell you?
BEE	But how did these skiing dead kids get down?
TRICIA	Similar way to the roller coaster. Only the chairlift things suddenly change course and go down.
MIRACLE	So, what they gonna say happened to us?
TRICIA	Oh, we'll probably be one of those 'School Bus Off Cliff' tragedies.
RAB	You talk the biggest pile of cack ever.

Shouts of agreement.

TRICIA	No, but no, shut up, right, no, shut up, listen right. I know it sounds stupid but I mean, it sounded stupid to me when I first heard it from the head of The British Intelligence…

TOM	You said you put two and two together.
TRICIA	Ah, well, my dear Tom, I'm afraid it's a bit more complicated than that. I am in fact a spy. Working under cover. Posing as just an ordinary schoolgirl, when actually I am Britain's last hope of exposing The Spirisy. I shouldn't be telling you this. I could be putting you all in mortal danger.

Pause.

JAMES	No. *(pause)* Carry on.
TRICIA	No. I mustn't. If the Nasties found out that you knew they'd probably murder you. Pull your heads off with this special new machine that, like, pulls your heads off. It, like, sort of twists it a bit…
JAMES	I'm gonna be a torture and killing machine designer when I'm older. I'm gonna design things like what you've never heard of. That, like, has little stabbing pins and sucks the jelly bit in your eyes out so they shrivel up and fall out and like, cuts this hole in your tummy and pulls out your guts and plucks your hairs out one by one, and, for like, old men, it would do your nostril hairs as well…
TOM	Yeah, but…
JAMES	No. Quiet. I'm talking. It pulls your fingers out and sticks sharp points up your nostrils that makes it bleed everywhere and it pierces your brain, and it's red hot – no, white hot – so it frazzles your brain but you don't die yet because your brain's not completely burned yet, and you can still feel pain. And sharp knives dig under you fingernails…

RAB	Is that before or after they've been pulled out?
JAMES	Shut up! *(his eyes widen into a terrifying glare)* Before. And then, when your brain's burned out completely, and your eyes have fallen out, and your fingers have been pulled out, then this claw will come out and it will chicken-scratch your heart until you're dead.

He rubs his hands and grins. The others look shocked.

RAB	*(sarcastically)* Nice job.
JAMES	Or I might be a doctor.

Pause.

BEN	You could be both. *(pause)* Being a doctor would give you access to people to test your equipment on.
JAMES	*(seeing it, dreamily)* A sick doctor...!
TRICIA	Has this got anything to do with what I was sayin'?
JAMES	You was talkin' about the Nasties' killing machine.
TRICIA	Yeah, but that doesn't mean that you can just go raving on like something out of Amityville. So shut it.
JAMES	Yeah, well someone nicked my Twix. I was annoyed, innit?
TRICIA	You're such a weirdo.
BEN	Don't, Tricia. His sadistic tendencies may be useful to us when we get to the centre of the earth.

TRICIA	Yeah, whatever.
CHRISSY	You ever been to a funeral?
BEE	Yeah.
CHRISSY	I've been to two funerals.
BEE	Yeah, I go to funerals every single Monday.
CHRISSY	Yeah, what happens, then?
BEE	They bury people, don't they.
CHRISSY	Yeah, but…
BEE	An' I go to bonfires, as well. That's when they put someone in the bonfire and watch them die slowly – and then laugh. And then they get all the ashes and make the relatives eat it.
SAM	Doesn't it taste 'orrible, though?
BEE	It tastes of them. Like, if I were to take a bite out of you now, I'd taste you and remember that taste, right, and then if someone burnt loads of people and put all their ashes in bowls, I could taste each one and see which one was you.
SAM	Really?
BEE	Yeah.
SAM	Shall we try it?
BEE	Ain't touchin' you.
SAM	I don't mean me.

Pause.

BEE, SAM & CHRISSY	Sonneeeee?

SONNY	Yeah?
BEE	Would you mind if we, erm… If we took a bite out of your leg and then burnt you with loads of other people and then tried you with a small spoon?
SONNY	*(after a moment's thought)* Go on, then.
BEE	You go first.
SAM	It was your idea.
BEE	No, I've done it so often.
SAM	Well, I don't want to lose my appetite. And anyway, they don't burn people.
BEE	They do. It's called cremations. Sometimes they give you the ashes to take home in pots; other times people leave it there, and it gets given to cannibal countries. They prefer it to Nescafe.
TOM	Cup-a-soup for cannibals. *(pause)* My dad's friend, who's a farmer…
SAM	Your dad's friend's not a farmer.
TOM	He is.
SAM	You dad hasn't got any friends.
TOM	He has.
SAM	You haven't got a dad.
TOM	I have! Like I was sayin', right, my dad's friend, who's a farmer…
SAM	Get on with it.
TOM	He got caught under a tractor.
JAMES	*(without sympathy)* Did he die? Did he?

42

TOM	No. He was alright.
JAMES	Yeah? Which bit of him got mashed?
TOM	His legs. He ain't got no legs no more.
BEE	What happened to his legs?
TOM	They got caught under the tractor, didn't they?
BEE	Yeah, but where are they now?
TOM	They probably buried them.
SAM	Yeah, you go to funerals. Ain't you ever seen legs buried?
BEE	No, they only bury whole bodies where I go.
JAMES	I've just had an idea.
SAM	What?
JAMES	Wouldn't it be cheaper to bury all your bits, like, separate, than buryin' them all together. And also you'd get to have loads of funerals, like, one for your leg and one for your head. And you could go to your own funeral. Not your head's funeral obviously – or your heart's. But you could probably bury a leg or two before you died of blood loss. And...
SAM	It wouldn't be cheaper because you'd have to buy loads of different-sized coffins. And they'd all have to be made specially to order, 'cos they don't normally make them different sizes for just ordinary people.
JAMES	Yeah. Some rich people get coffins for their cats and dogs. I'd need two dog ones, one for each leg; and two cat ones for my arms. And a small sheep one for my middle bit.

MATTHEW	Buryin' bits separate would be a good idea to find out who really cared about you. It'd be a good idea for my mum 'cos she's always pretendin' to suicide herself to see if we care…
SAM	And do you?
MATTHEW	We pretend we do. *(with pride)* If you've got a mad mum like me, you have to have a man from the council round every week to check on you.
SAM	*(impressed)* Wow.
CHRISSY	Oh yeah, I get that too, since my dad went to prison.
SAM	What's your dad in prison for?
CHRISSY	Oh, lots of stuff. *(pause)* Mainly 'cos he killed this man.
JAMES	Rah! That's so cool.
SAM	How did he do it? How did he do it?
CHRISSY	*(nonchalantly)* Strangled him with his bare hands.
TOM	Cor. I wish my dad was cool.
ANNA	What's it like down there, Tricia?
TRICIA	Down there? On the floor of the coach? I dunno. It's sort of…
ANNA	No, the centre of the earth. Will there be any lights? I can't go to sleep without a light on.
TRICIA	Well, yeah. Of course the Nasties are gonna make sure that there's some light, otherwise they won't be able to see us through the video cameras to watch how we live.

ANNA	So there will be some light?
TRICIA	Yeah. There will be light. But wouldn't you rather live a life of darkness than know that you're being watched day after day, night after night?
ANNA	Er... Well, no. You see, I can't go to sleep without a light.
TRICIA	Oh yeah. You said.
STACEY	*(to James)* I don't think Miracle's got a TV.
CHRISSY & BEE	What!
STACEY	All that rubbish about War of the Worlds. I reckon she hasn't got one.
CHRISSY	Yeah, and she reckoned the reason Alfie was vexed was because Kat was doing sex with someone!
STACEY & BEE	*(amazed)* No!
BEE	*(leaning in to the conversation)* When I went to her house she said it was at the mender's.
STACEY	How long ago was this?
BEE	About three months ago.
JAMES	She ain't got a TV? Oi, Rab. Get this. Miracle ain't got a telly!
RAB	Rah! Miracle! Are you a tramp or what? *(in front of the whole coach)* Ain't you got a telly?

Everyone laughs.

MIRACLE	What?

JAMES	You ain't got a telly!
MIRACLE	Of course I do.
JAMES	Oo yeah.
MIRACLE	I do.
RAB	Alright then. How does the Muller advert go, then?
MIRACLE	Isn't that the one when… There's the mum at the breakfast…
EVERYONE	NO! 5-6-7-8… Got my hair, got my head, got my brains, got my ears, got my eyes, got my nose, got my mouth, got my smile. Got my tongue, got my chin, got my bum, got my boobs, got my heart, got my soul, got my liver, got my sex. I got my freedom, freedom. I got life.
RAB	Lead a Muller Life!
EVERYONE	T-E-L-L-Y-T-E-L-L-Y-T-E-L-L-Y. You ain't got a telly!

*The chant gets faster and faster and more and more in **Miracle**'s face. They keep repeating until she breaks down.*

MIRACLE	*(through terrible sobs)* You don't know what it's like. My mum won't let me have one. She says it rots your brain. She makes me do stuff in the garden and draw and read and play the saxophone instead. She's so horrible. She's like a witch. I hate her so much.
TRICIA	Miracle, don't worry. It's not that bad. *(pause, then she declares loudly)* I haven't got one either.
MIRACLE	Really?

JAMES	*(to **Tricia**)* Urggh, you filthy tramp. Get back in your cardboard box.

*Everyone starts teasing **Tricia**.*

JENELLE	Oh my God! Shut up! Can anyone else hear that ticking?

*The paranoia builds up as they search for the source of the ticking, finally traced to… **Rab**.*

RAB	Boom!

Screams.

JENELLE	That is not even funny, Rab. Now that we know Miss Sheehankov is a terrorist you shouldn't make jokes like that…
SAM	Jenelle, don't worry. They need us to be alive… so they can watch us, right, Trish?
TOM	Brainwash us, more like.
RAB	*(popping up)* Shut up, Tom. Loser!
TRICIA	No, Rab. He's right. I didn't want to say this. But the experiment isn't to watch us. The experiment is to brainwash us. To turn us in to Nasties.
JENELLE	Why?
TRICIA	So that we will end up like Miss Sheehankov. Pretending to be a nice teacher what supports Arsenal so that we can capture more kids to brainwash. It's a vikkious cycle.
MIRACLE	What are we gonna do, Trish?

TRICIA	We'll make a break for it when we're down there, and hide out in this cave I know about that the terrorists don't know and keep guard...
JENELLE	Will we have someone on guard all night for the Nasties?
TRICIA	Er... Yeah.
JENELLE	Do I have to do it, Tricia? I don't think girls should have to do it.
TRICIA	No, sorry. Everyone has to do it.
JAMES	*(popping up)* I'll do it. It'll be like Tomb Raider.

He mimes shooting up Nasties with deadly precision.

> Mega death.

He mimes gore and blood splatter-fest.

JENELLE	Can I be partners with you, James? I think I'll feel safest with you.
JAMES	*(suddenly shy and coy)* Yeah, alright. If you like.
SONNY	Jenelle? Don't you want to be partners with me?

Pause.

ANNA	Tricia, I've been doing some serious thinking. We've got to try and take control of this situation. We can't let them put us on that roller coaster. I can't live in the centre of the earth. I have some tictacs – I mean tactics.
TRICIA	You? You're scared of the dark!

ANNA	Well, it's time for me to grow up.
RAB	*(whose face has been wedged between the two seats throughout the entire conversation)* Waaaah! I can't believe that you think all this cack is actually true!
ANNA	It could be true. It could be true. We don't know. Nobody knows.

Everyone is now listening.

	We know that terrorists want to kill us and that they live in caves. We know that Harris and Sheehankov were talking in code. We know that purple is the terrorist code to 'kill the children'...
JENELLE	...And that the Funny Mentalists are doing bombings...
SONNY	...And that the Nasties were never actually killed and are running the whole Spirisy...
STACEY	...And that behind them is the North Koreans...
JAMES	...And that they have to brainwash us to turn us into terrorists...
ANNA	Yeah. And Tricia heard it from the head of The British Intelligence. If you can't trust the head of The British Intelligence then who can you trust?
MIRACLE	Exactly.
TOM	But who's behind the North Koreans?
MIRACLE	Lets ask Tricia?
STACEY	Tricia, who's behind the North Koreans?
TRICIA	The most terrifying creature you can imagine.

Like a jellyfish octopus brain thing with tentacles and massive sharp long teeth. The size of... London. It lives right at the very centre of the earth and its tentacles reach all the way through the caves and networks that the Nasties have built, and instead of suckers there are cameras all over his tentacles which are watching everyone all the time to see how the brainwashing is going.

RAB *(suspiciously)* What's its name?

TRICIA Its name is... Doctor Al Kiyeeder!

Gasps.

RAB So that's who Al Kiyeeder is! Oh my days – it is true.

BEN I think it is true.

JAMES He speaks...

MIRACLE Shut up, James. Let him have his say.

RAB Shup. You ain't got a telly.

MIRACLE What d'you think's true, Mr Bean?

BEN I think it is very possible that the terrorists could actually be living in the centre of the earth. Tricia's accounts have, in fact, been most accurate.

RAB Tricia's whats have been what?

TRICIA How would you know? I mean, they have been, but how the hell do you know that?

BEN *(pause)* I've been there.

TRICIA Shut up.

50

ANNA	How did you get down?
BEN	In a chairlift. Like Tricia said.
TRICIA	You can't of done.
ANNA	Is there any light?
TRICIA	I've already told you that there is.
ANNA	Well, yes, but I mean, Ben's actually been there, so he's more likely to know for sure, isn't he?
BEN	Don't worry, Anna. There is some light. Things produce their own natural light. Like glow-worms.
ANNA	Oh, good.
TRICIA	He doesn't know what he's talkin' about.
CHRISSY	He's been there. You've only heard about it from The British Intelligence.
TRICIA	I have been there.
BEN	Oh? What is it like, then?
TRICIA	Well, the area I went to, known as... Erm... Lower Beemsbry, was made up of these huge caves. Dark, 'cept for when the light from the glow-worms shone on the bits of jewels in the walls. Lower Beemsbry is like the capital... 'Cos it's the most beautiful area. There were dark passages everywhere, like corridors, leading off into different rooms. The floor's soft and sandy – it's actually jewel dust – so it sparkles. When I came back I still had some jewel dust on my shoes...
RAB	Let's see.
TRICIA	It's rubbed off now, stupid. Anyway, there are

glow-worms, like Ben said. And glow-maggots. And the Nasties have glow-eels. I slept in one of the small caves – I had a huge, flat rock as a bedside table. I was only there for two days.

*Everyone looks at **Ben** for confirmation.*

ANNA	Ben?
BEN	It's nothing like that. And there's no glow-eels.
RAB	Mmmm. Nice imagination, Trish.
TOM	It's too hot down there.
BEN	Not if you wear this stuff called 'Starlite' that a hairdresser in Manchester invented. A suit of Starlite, you could sit on the sun and be OK – on the surface only, obviously. No one believed this hairdresser. The Starlite was mouldable like plastic and yet virtually completely heatproof. Impossible, scientists said. But they tested it, and the lazer they tested it with – which burns through slabs of iron in a millisecond – broke due to the reflection of heat. It was on television, but it was on BBC2 so none of you will have watched it. Hairdresser. In Manchester.

Pause.

ANNA	*(who appears to have been thinking hard)* Miss! Miss! Is Alton Towers near Manchester?
MISS SHEEHAN	*(from the far end of the coach, unseen)* Yes, not far!

The children look at each other for a tense moment.

JENELLE	Wow.

| TRICIA | Mr Bean's lying. |
| ANNA | Ben is not lying. |

*When **Ben** pauses, he looks at his audience through his extra-strong lens glasses and sucks meditatively on his pencil.*

TRICIA	He is. I'm the spy. I know what's going on. Ben's just makin' it up. He's never been there.
BEN	Unlike you. I'm not one to boast about my part in such a serious affair as this.
TRICIA	Just 'cos you can say lots of stupid words that don't mean anything to anyone, you think you're really cool.
ANNA	What do we sleep on?
BEN	Erm... Oh, well, when I was there we slept on... Erm... Rocks.
MIRACLE	How uncomfortable. Was it really bad?
TRICIA	Don't be ridiculous. They're trying to brainwash you in to being like them. And I bet you they won't be sleeping on rocks.
BEN	That's what I was about to say. I went before the terrorists had set up this experiment. *(pause)* I was the first ever person there.
TRICIA	The brainwashing laboratory was set up in 1936. November. That's before you were born.
BEN	Ah, yes. But the west side of the centre of the earth. Not the bit that everyone goes to. *(pause)* If you know so much about all this, tell me the name of the North Korean terrorist spy who is in charge.

TRICIA	Radkot Flipscoddle.
MIRACLE	That doesn't sound North Korean.
TRICIA	Obviously. It's a codename. *(pause)* Alright then, what's his real name?

Ben hesitates for a moment.

TRICIA	You don't know.
BEN	No, I'm just wondering whether it's wise to tell you. *(pause)* How do I know you are really who you say you are?
TRICIA	Oh, this is stupid. I know you're lying. You know you're lying. So why bother?
ANNA	You just wanna have all the attention, Tricia. You just wanna be the one who knows it all. And you can't stand it when someone knows more than you, can you?
TRICIA	*(shouting)* It's got nothing to do with that! I know he's lying.
STACEY	So he's lying and you're not? Is that it? Everything you say goes. Everything he says is cack? Is that it?
TRICIA	No, that's not it.
CHRISSY	Well, that's certainly what it seems like, Tricia.
TRICIA	Piss off, Chrissy. This has got nothin' to do with you.
ANNA	This has got everything to do with Chrissy and everyone else in class 4S. It's all of us that have gotta face this.
MATTHEW	Maybe it's the time for the revolution!

STACEY	What's that?
MATTHEW	It's something they do the whole time in history. My mum's always on about it.
RAB	Yeah, but your mum's a loonytune.
MATTHEW	Only 'cos the revolution hasn't come yet.
STACEY	Well, how do you do one?
MATTHEW	You just, like, stop doing what anyone tells you. And throw stones and stuff. And like, demand your rights…
CHRISSY	What's our rights?
JAMES	Not to be kidnapped by evil terrorists what are pretending to be nice teachers for a start…
SAM	Rah man, I totally believed that she supported Arsenal, you know…
TRICIA	*(shouting)* Will you all just shut up and listen to me? I know that Ben is lying because… Because I made it up.
RAB	What, about Sheehankov supporting Arsenal?
TRICIA	No. About going to the centre of the earth.

Long silence.

ANNA	Tricia, we all know you're tryin' to protect us from findin' out too much for our own safety – and it's very good of you – but now I think it's time that we all faced facts. Don't you?

Long pause.

TRICIA	Yes. It's time. You're right. And it was for your

protection. I should of known I couldn't fool you lot.

ANNA   So, Mr Bean. Are you a spy?

BEN   Well, as a matter of fact, *(pause)* yes, I am.

*As everyone crowds around **Ben**, **Tricia** sulks in the background. Her arms are folded, and whenever **Ben** says something she shakes her head scornfully.*

STACEY   Surely, you shouldn't say that in case one of us is a terrorist spy.

BEN   Yes, *(pause)* and I have my suspicions.

*He nods towards **Tricia**, who has her back to him.*

STACEY   *(whispering)* Tricia?

ANNA & STACEY   No.

BEN   *(leaning in to his eager listeners)* The name she gave of the terrorist leader?

ANNA & STACEY   Yes?

BEN   She said it was the codename?

ANNA & STACEY   Yes?

BEN   The British don't know that codename. It's something we've been trying to discover for years.

STACEY   Then how come she knows it?

BEN   I wonder.

ANNA   If it is true, then she'll try and warn Sheehankov. Try and tell her that we know.

56

STACEY	How long 'till we're there?
BEN	*(looking at his watch)* Taking account of the late departure... Twelve minutes, seventeen seconds and... Twenty-six milliseconds.
ANNA	Twelve minutes. We have no time to lose.

Rab and James can be heard screeching with laughter from behind the seats.

JAMES	Look! Look!

James produces one of the see-through sick bags, which appears to be full of vomit.

RAB	*(leaning over and pretending to be violently sick into the bag)* I've been sick!

He passes the bag around for closer inspection.

BEE	I'm gonna make one too.

She rummages around in her packed lunch, looking for things with which to concoct another bag of sick.

JENELLE	I'm actually gonna be sick. Miss! I'm gonna be sick!

Bee and Rab waft the fake sick in Jenelle's face, while making sick noises.

MISS SHEEHAN	The next one of you to do that will have to eat it.
EVERYONE	Urghh.
TRICIA	Yeah. But it's all mashed up.

JENELLE	I'm not jokin'. I'm gonna be sick. Get me a sick bag – quick!
MIRACLE	They're all filled with mashed-up pack lunch!
JENELLE	Just get me anything! Quick!
ANNA	Here's one.

*She hands **Jenelle** one of the see-through sick bags. **Jenelle** attempts to open the bag, but it's one of those plastic ones that stick together and you can't tell which end is which.*

ANNA	*(desperate)* I can't get it open!

*Eventually **Jenelle** manages to open it, and is sick – much to everyone's enjoyment.*

RAB	Look! Look! She 'ad egg for breakfast. She was the one who guffed!
JAMES	Oi. Leave her alone.
EVERYONE	Oooooooooo.
RAB	Excuse me, Miss. But Jenelle's just done exactly what you told us not to. She's put all her pack lunch – all mashed up – into a sick bag!
CHRISSY	Miss said the next one would have to eat it.
RAB	*(triumphantly)* I know.
BEE	That is pure jokes!
SONNY & JAMES	Leave her alone!

They glare at each other.

MIRACLE	*(warning)* Sheehankov's coming!

MISS SHEEHAN	Jenelle, did you do what I told you not to?
JENELLE	No, it's really sick, Miss.
CHRISSY	Rab was tryin' to get Jenelle into trouble.
MISS SHEEHAN	Well, then Rab can eat it.
RAB	No, Miss!

*Everyone has burst out laughing and is pushing the bag of sick towards **Rab**.*

No! Please, Miss. That's not funny. It's not even my sick! I don't like egg! Please, Miss. I was jokin'. Please, Miss, don't make me, Miss! *(he is almost in tears)* I'm sorry.

MISS SHEEHAN	Alright, that's enough.

*Everyone reluctantly withdraws from **Rab**.*

RAB	Thanks, Miss Sheehankov – erm, Sheehan. Sorry, I meant Sheehan.

*Everyone is glaring at **Rab** when he turns back to face them.*

I slipped.

TOM	You slipped? You slipped? You idiot! You fool. Now Miss Sheehankov knows that we know. There's no chance of escape now!
MIRACLE	Look! Look! She's talking to the coach driver. She's telling him that we know.
TOM	There's no hope. You idiot!
ANNA	We should make plans.
RAB	I'm really sorry.

TOM   OK. Apology accepted. Now, come on. Let's
             decide what we're gonna do.

Jenelle suddenly bursts into tears.

JENELLE   I'm scared.

SONNY   *(putting his arm around her)* Don't worry, Jenelle.
             It's all gonna be fine.

ANNA   Jenelle. Keep it down. If Sheehankov hears you
             she'll be over here like a shot.

MIRACLE   *(hissing)* She's coming!

Everyone quickly sits back in their seats.

JAMES   *(smiling sweetly)* Hello, Miss.

MISS SHEEHAN Are you alright, Jenelle? Do you want to come
              and sit at the front for a bit?

Bee shakes her head, scared stiff.

SONNY   I'm looking after her, Miss. She's safe with me.

MISS SHEEHAN So, Anna, what are you going to go on when
              we finally get there?

Anna stares up at her, terrified.

MISS SHEEHAN What about the waterslide?

ANNA   Yes. The waterslide is fun.

MISS SHEEHAN And The Blackhole? I guess everyone will be
              going on that.

Anna catches Ben's eye.

ANNA	*(quietly)* Yeah… I don't think I will be going on the Blackhole… Miss.
MISS SHEEHAN	Oh, I'm sure you will, Anna. I'm going to make it my personal duty to get you all on that roller coaster. Seeing you all screaming your little heads off will make the whole trip worthwhile.
ANNA	Oh, right. See you later, Miss.

All look at each other as **Miss Sheehan** *returns to her seat.*

MIRACLE	She knows.
RAB	*(to* **Anna***)* What's the plan?
ANNA	We are going to have to get control of the coach.
BEN	Five minutes, fifty-two seconds, twelve milliseconds.
ANNA	Is everyone in agreement?

Solemn nods.

TRICIA	Don't be stupid. We can't do that. We're only kids. Can anyone drive? I mean, it's stupid. It's impossible. We are just gonna stay calm and see how it goes.

Ben *looks at* **Anna** *as if to say 'see?'.*

ANNA	Tricia. I'm beginning to wonder whose side you're on. First you tell us you're a British spy with nerves of iron…
TRICIA	I didn't say nothin' about any iron…
ANNA	And now it seems that you're a terrorist, helping the Nasties to capture us.

| CHRISSY | (suddenly lashing out at **Tricia**, hysterical) You filthy terrorist spy! You traitor! I can't believe I invited you to my birthday party! There's gonna be no traitors at my birthday party! |

Chrissy breaks down in sobs.

TRICIA	Chrissy! I'm not a terrorist spy. I'm not any sort of spy!
BEN	As I suspected.
TRICIA	(almost screaming) Shut up! You're the evil one! You deserve to die!

Anna grabs hold of **Tricia** by the shoulders.

| ANNA | Shut up! You're hysterical! Sheehankov will be here any moment. Now, everyone just stay calm. Jenelle, do you need another sick bag? |

Jenelle nods.

| SONNY & JAMES | I'll get one! |

Sonny and **James** tussle over the sick bag. **Sonny** eventually wins.

MISS SHEEHAN	(from her seat, unseen) What's going on back there?
EVERYONE	Nothin', Miss.
SONNY	A sick bag, Jenelle!
JENELLE	Thank you, Sonny.

She is violently sick.

ANNA	Now we need to decide who's in charge of what.
JAMES	Rab an' me'll be in charge of the battle tactics.
RAB	Now, has everyone got weapons?
TOM	Oh yeah. I'll just get my Kalashnikov out of my backpack. You fool. 'Course we haven't got weapons.
MIRACLE	What do we need 'em for, anyway?
SAM	This thing has gotta be done using surprise tactics and weapons.
JENELLE	Well, none of us got any knives or nothin' so what d'you suggest?
MATTHEW	Pack-lunch boxes? I mean, anything that will hurt if it hits you.
MIRACLE	Satsumas. My mum packed five. Vitamin C.

Miracle passes the satsumas around.

ANNA	Right, Tom, I'm making you head of communications.
RAB	But he's a der-brain.
ANNA	Rab, it's time to pull together now. We can't afford to be fighting with each other.

Rab has to agree, and he and Tom hug manfully.

ANNA	Right, 4S. Are you with me?
EVERYONE	Sir, yes sir!
ANNA	I didn't hear you.
EVERYONE	Sir, yes sir!

ANNA	So, James, Rab. How do you suggest we take over the coach?
JAMES	Rab an' me'll crawl to the front of the coach an' get ready behind the driver.
TOM	Chrissy should go too – her dad's a killer.
RAB	Affirmative. Then you lot, after countin' to ten...
SAM	Silently.
JAMES	Yeah, obviously. Anyway...
TOM	If we all suddenly go silent they'll know something's going on.
MIRACLE	Go on, James.
ANNA	No, Tom is head of communications and he's right. It needs to be better planned.
MIRACLE	How long have we got?
BEN	Two minutes, twenty-one seconds, forty milliseconds.
ANNA	Tom, what do you think?
TOM	I think it would be better, if we sing a song and then arrange a certain point...
JAMES	Yeah, whatever. Anyway, when you get to this certain point, we'll all charge to the front and attack Sheehankov...
TRICIA	NO!
ANNA	Is there a problem with this plan?
TRICIA	Yes. What if Miss Sheehankov – I mean Miss Sheehan – isn't a terrorist, after all?

MIRACLE	If she's not a terrorist then why's she taking us the centre of the earth?
TRICIA	Maybe she's not.
TOM	Forty-two seconds. What are we gonna sing?
MIRACLE	*(to **Tricia**)* Why d'you think that?
TRICIA	I made it all up.

*Miracle looks at the crowd of excited children and then back to **Tricia**.*

MIRACLE	Why?
JENELLE	What about Crazy Frog?
TRICIA	*(to **Miracle**)* I s'pose, to make you all like me.
TOM	Three times through.

Pause.

MIRACLE	Do you really not have a telly?
TRICIA	No, I do. I just said that so they'd stop picking on you.
MIRACLE	That's the nicest thing anyone's ever done for me.
TOM	*(looking at watch, whispering loudly)* 12, 11, 10…

The others excitedly join in.

EVERYONE	9, 8, 7…
MIRACLE	*(suddenly standing)* Stop! Tricia needs to tell us something very important!

*A pause. The children look questioningly at **Miracle**.*

TRICIA	You mustn't do this… There's no terrorists. Miss Sheehan does support Arsenal. I don't know anyone from The Head of British Intelligence…
ANNA	Yeah, exactly. Cos Ben's the spy. Not you.

Pause.

BEN	Tricia's right. We're not spies. You can't live in the centre of the earth, even with a suit of Starlite…
TRICIA	The queen is probably not even a lizard…

Pause.

JAMES	It's a common problem. I've seen it many times in battle. They're cracking up under the pressure. Don't worry about it. Keep counting!
EVERYONE	5, 4, 3, 2, 1

They burst in to the Crazy Frog anthem.

MIRACLE	*(panicking)* My mum says that when you're feeling overexcited you should sit down and breathe calmly!
MATTHEW	I thought you said you hate your mum.
MIRACLE	I know… And now I realise that I love her more than anything in the world.

*Tricia grabs **Sonny's** arm as **Sonny** begins to sing.*

TRICIA	Sonny! You've got to stop them. You know I make stuff up all the time! Tell them! You're my best friend!

Sonny   You're not my friend, Tricia. I'll never forgive you for telling Jenelle that I love her.

*Everyone continues singing as **Rab** and **James** crawl to the front of the bus. They hide behind the driver each armed with a packed lunch box and a satsuma. As the children get towards the end of the third time through they begin to sing in loud, excited voices.*

Tric., Ben &   MISS SHEEHAN!
Mir.

Anna   Stop them!

*The children tackle and tie up and gag **Tricia**, **Ben** and **Miracle**.*

***Tricia** and **Ben** catch eyes and stare at each other. Suddenly the other children charge towards the audience, shrieking. **Sonny** glances back at **Tricia**. He pauses for a moment, then continues running. They attack **Miss Sheehan** and the driver.*

James   *(while attaching the driver)* Take that, you North Korean Funny Mentalist Jellyfish Lizard Nastie! Think you could fool us, did you?

Suddenly it seems that the children are back on their imaginary roller coaster, swerving and lurching. All face the audience, their faces full of fear and excitement.

Rab   Waaaaah!

Jenelle   Woooooh!

James   Wickeeeeed!

Anna   Arrrghghhghghgh!

End.

Staging the play

 ## SET

You can create the interior of a coach using genuine coach seats; or you could stage the play by adopting a less naturalistic approach with whatever seating you can find. You'll see this is the way Daisy and Ken Campbell have imagined the staging would operate. Inside the script are lots of suggestions as to how the chairs might be positioned. Take these as a useful guideline, but you might come up with different solutions.

You might use a mixture of chairs; ones with wheels can be useful. Whatever you choose make sure they're light as well as robust. The more scope they will offer for leaning on and adopting a variety of positions, the better.

 ## LIGHTING

Avoid introducing projections to suggest the outside passing scenery. It's much more important to concentrate on the imaginative world that is being created inside the coach. If you have a choice of playing space consider placing the action inside a black box theatre or studio so the focus remains firmly on the actors.

Keep the lighting as simple as possible; just make sure the actors' faces can be seen at all times. You might want to do something a little different when Anna and Stacey interrogate Ben on page 56. You could use something as simple as an angle poise, the girls could each hold a torch or even swing a light bulb between them. Avoid blackouts, have the actors make the scene changes as interesting to watch as the scenes themselves.

☞♫ SOUND

Songs such as 'Can't Fool the Children of the Revolution' by T.Rex could be used to help cover the scene changes. This (and any other song you use) is intended to be sung and hummed in a comic way by the actors. Avoid pre-recorded music during the show (though you might want to choose something appropriate to warm the atmosphere as the audience settle).

Don't be tempted to give the adult role of Miss Sheehan to an actor who is visible to the audience. It's really important that all of the focus is on the children. Let's imagine Miss Sheehan and the coach driver. Create the voice of Miss Sheehan with an actor and an offstage microphone. Don't get bogged down with pre-recording the voice and timing the cues. It's far better to play it live.

☞ COSTUME

If you stage the play you will need to decide whether all of the visible characters are in uniform for the journey or in their own clothes. If you give them a basic school uniform it would be fun to add some touches which define their personality. How they wear their uniform could tell us a lot, even their choice of lunchbox will say something about their personality

and background. Look at this photo from an earlier production of the play. Try and identify the characters the actors are playing.

PROPS

Keep these to an absolute minimum. Have fun with the content of the sick bags (a mixture of condensed soups works quite nicely) and make sure they're sealed.

CUES

The class know each other really well and have a fast rapport with one another. It's important that cues are picked up really quickly. Get into the good habit of listening and reacting quickly.

Speaking and listening activity

In a circle one person whispers a message to the person next to them. This person passes the message on but distorts and confuses the facts. Repeat this process right around the circle. The last person to receive the message speaks it out loud to everyone else and it can now be compared to the first message. See how it has been exaggerated.

CREATING INTERESTING STAGE PICTURES

The positioning of the actors on the stage is of obvious importance when staging the play. Use the following activities to find the most effective way of presenting the play to the audience.

Drama activity

In groups of five

1   Each person pick up a chair and, on a pre-arranged signal, form a conventional coach-seating pattern. Experiment with a series of states such as coach in profile, coach seen from the front, from behind and above.

continued

---

2 Create an aisle that is linear; see what difference it makes if you increase the width of the aisle.

3 Experiment with different types of chairs: try introducing some that can be wheeled or swivelled. Practice sitting, lying and kneeling on the chairs. Discover what happens when all five are kneeling, lying or sitting at the same time. These levels are going to be useful when you come to stage the play. Be very aware of your audience and make sure everyone can see the action at all times.

4 Look at the scene between Anna, Ben and Stacey starting on page 56. Rehearse it using wheelie chairs. Move in and out of scenes as swiftly as possible but begin by rehearsing them in slow motion. Try to choose the most direct route. Move with certainty. Once you are sure of where you and the chair are travelling to and from, speed up the action.

Look at the entrances and exits into and out of the other scenes. Vary the direction the actors are coming from. Use your acting space as creatively as you can, make each scene an interesting stage picture.

FINDING THE FOCUS

This is quite a large ensemble piece with a lot of characters on stage all of the time. It's going to be really important for the audience to see and hear who's talking at any given moment. The other actors can help the audience focus by concentrating, listening and sometimes (but not always) looking at the actors who are speaking. Look at the photograph of an earlier production of the play where Sonny is embarrassed by the others on page 19. How has he been made the focus at this moment?

If you choose to move the chairs around rather than recreating a static coach, allow the characters at the centre of the scene a good position in the acting space. Centre stage is strong but you'll want to vary this. It's important not to overuse the same entrance points and areas of the stage.

ANIMATING THE PLAY

You may find it useful to imagine these larger than life characters are lifted straight out of a cartoon.

Drama activity

1 As the class (from the play), imagine Miss Sheehan is passing through the coach. You can make general noise that falls to silence as she passes. Follow her with your eyes as if you are one person.

2 Have Miss Sheehan walk the aisle slowly and upright, slowly and crouching, have her make herself thin and then large. See what happens to the class's focus.

3 In groups of five, form a section of the coach. Improvise the coach departing, the coach going over bumps, travelling at high speed, coach at night time, coach breaking suddenly etc.

4 Have one of the group 'conduct' the other four as a roller coaster by taking them through the ride's twists and turns, highs and lows, scary and safe moments etc. Now look at the scene where the class re-enact The Corkscrew (on pages 21–24) and run it using some of the ideas you used in this improvisation.

5 Imagine the coach journey is being filmed from a variety of angles. As a group, turn round, sit down walk about making sure you're in the camera shot all the time.

One way of acting out the roller coaster scene.

Work on and around the script

CHARACTERS

1   Draw up a list of facts you know about the key characters based on what you've read in the script. Take James for instance.

> Character: *James*
>
> ### What we know about him
>
> *He likes talking about gory events.*
>
> *He's an expert on horror movies.*
>
> ### Things he makes up
>
> *He's going to be a torture and killing machine designer when he grows up.*
>
> ### Other things that might be true about him
>
> *(These come from Daisy Campbell)*
>
> *He might live with just his Mum.*
>
> *At home he might be very tame.*

The class refer to a number of television characters such as Pat Butcher in EastEnders. Mr Bean is named after a popular comedy character portrayed by the actor Rowan Atkinson.

Rowan Atkinson as Mr Bean.

It's good to understand these reference points, not least because it tells us about the characters' tastes in television. They clearly watch a lot because they even know the tunes from the commercials.

The fact Miracle doesn't have a TV at all is a big issue and the focus of a scene. Tricia steps in to protect Miracle from the others' teasing and this shows us that Tricia has a sympathetic nature. This action wins her Miracle's affection.

Pam St. Clement as Pat Butcher from EastEnders.

PLAYING EIGHT YEAR OLDS.

If you are staging the play, it may be useful to visit a primary school.

Improvisation

In groups, of five and in role as eight year olds, move as one body in a clump (definitely not a line). Take the lead from the person at the front. Throughout this impro, and without discussion, another leader needs to take over at regular intervals.

Imagine you are on a journey to the centre of the earth. Each new leader can change the situation to include for instance a crocodile swamp, a swinging rope bridge over a hundred foot ravine, a red hot desert etc.

FACTS BEHIND THE SCRIPT

School Journey to the Centre of the Earth borrows its title from a classic novel by Jules Verne published in 1864 and later made into a film. Below is a still from the 1959 version.

In it, an ancient parchment bearing a mysterious cryptogram maps the most hazardous journey of Professor Lidenbrock's career. With his nephew and a guide the Professor travels to Iceland. Their journey to the centre of the earth begins on the summit of a volcano and takes them down through secret passages, across a desolate underground sea populated by prehistoric marine monsters, on what may be a voyage of no return.

It seems possible that Tricia may have seen the film (or perhaps a cartoon version), helping her to generate her fantasy. If you look at popular fiction, films and TV, the idea of a hidden world is extremely popular. Secret worlds and parallel universes can be found in everything from *Gulliver's Travels* and *Alice in Wonderland* to the Harry Potter series, via Phillip Pullman's *Northern Lights* trilogy. There are literally endless examples!

Class discussion and writing task

In groups

1   For five minutes, make a list of other books, films and TV programmes that contain a hidden world. Be prepared to share your findings with the class.

2   What else do these books and films have in common? Why do you think that fantasy works are so popular?

3   Either:

Imagine that you have been asked to create a pilot for a TV series about an imaginary world. Write a short (one page) synopsis of the idea that you would submit. You might include details of:

a.   What it's like there – how is it different to the real world?

continued

---

b. how you get to it

c. who lives there and what they do

d. if this world has any connection with ours.

Or:

Write a review of a book, film or TV programme that you have read or seen that deals with an imaginary world. You might include:

a. a very brief synopsis of the plot

b. a description of the imaginary world

c. what you liked about it (if anything)

d. what you disliked about it (if anything).

Themes in an around the play

TRUTH AND FANTASY

In an interview with Ken and Daisy by Jim Mulligan, Daisy admitted she had created a "Just William" character with Tricia. 'William could put ideas in all the Outlaws' heads so easily and so convincingly that they believed there was treasure in the back of the garden and would go digging there'. In the play Tricia makes the other schoolchildren believe Miss Sheehan is a terrorist.

In this extract from *Just William* by Richmal Crompton, William and the outlaws decide to raise money to buy a bow and arrow by charging admission to an animal show to be presented in William's bedroom.

The show had been widely advertised and all the neighbouring children had been individually canvassed, but under strict orders of secrecy. The threats of what the Outlaws would do if their secret were disclosed had kept many a child awake at night. William surveyed the room proudly.

"Not a bad show for a penny, I should say. I guess there aren't many like that, anyway. Do shut up talkin', Ginger. It'll spoil it all, if folks hear the giant talking out of his stomach. It's Douglas that's got to do the giant's talking. Anyone could see that. I say, they're comin'! Look! They're comin'! Along the wall!"

There was a thin line of children climbing along the wall in single file on all fours. They ascended the scullery roof and approached the window. These were the first arrivals who had called on their way to Sunday school.

Henry took their pennies and William cleared his throat and began:

"White rat from China, ladies and gentlemen, pink an' blue striped. All rats is pink an' blue striped in China. This is the only genwin China rat in England– brought over from China special last week jus' for the show. It lives on China bread and butter brought over special too."

"Wash it!" jeered an unbeliever. "Jus wash it an let's see it then."

"Wash it?" repeated the showman indignantly. "It's gotter be washed. It's washed every morning an' night the same as you or me. China rats have gotter be washed or they'll die right off. Washin' em don't make no difference to their stripes. Anyone knows that that knows anything about China rats I guess."

He laughed scornfully and turned to Smuts. Smuts had grown used to the basket chair and was settling down for a nap. William crouched down on all fours, ran his finger along the basket-work, and putting his face closed to it, gave vent to a malicious howl. Smuts sprang at him, scratching and spitting.

"Wild cat," said William triumphantly. "Look at it! Kill anyone if it got out! Spring at their throats, it would, an' scratch their eyes out with its paws an' bite their necks till its teeth met. If I us' moved away that chair it would spring out at you." They moved hastily away from the chair. "And I bet some of you would be dead pretty quick. It could have anyone's head right off with bitin' and scratchin'. Right off – separate from their bodies!"

There was an awe-stricken silence.

Then:

"Garn! It's Smuts. It's your sister's cat!"

William laughed as though vastly amused by this idea.

"Smuts!" he said, giving a surreptitious kick to the chair that infuriated its occupant still more. "I guess there wouldn't be many of us left in this house if Smuts was like this."

Compare this extract with the scene where Tricia tells everyone they're going to the centre of the earth (on page 14 from '**James** (*popping up*) Oi do you wanna hear the sickest thing ever?' to the bottom of page 16: '**Everyone** Oo-oh'.

Class discussion

1   In the first extract William is very sure of himself. Tricia can be a little hesitant at times. In what ways are William and Tricia similar and dissimilar?

2   Why do you think both William and Tricia fantasise?

3   What is the difference between lying and fantasising?

4   What qualities do they both have which make them leaders?

Tricia is a little bit like Daisy was. In the same interview she said, 'I used to go around the playground saying I was the Yingo-Yong. I had five layers of skin and every time anyone touched me I would lose a layer until I became a skeleton. The others really believed it. Like Tricia, I used to test the limits to see how far I could take them.' Unfortunately for Tricia, she oversteps the limits. And when Ben joins in she really is in trouble.

BEING QUICK-WITTED

Look at pages 50–55 where Tricia loses her power and control and Ben uses his intelligence to develop the fantasy. A good deal of fast thinking and invention is coming out of both of them. Decide why it is Ben who the others believe.

OLD AND NEW VERSIONS

This is not the first version of the play to have been published (or performed). The first version appeared in 1994. Because it is so full of references to TV programmes and events from the news, it was important to workshop the original and find out what needed updating. Take a look at this scene and compare it with the new version on pages 35–38 which begins with Stacey and 'yeah!'.

Jonathan How do you get down to the centre of the Earth? I mean, how would you, supposin' we was going' which I don't believe anyway.

Tricia Ah, well. That's the cunning bit. You know the roller-coaster at Alton Towers?

Louise	Yeah. The Corkscrew.
Rab	Yes it's wicked, man.
Hal	Yeah, that bit when it dips down is blindin'.
Tricia	Yeah, well anyway. Miss Sheehankov will give…
Louise	Sheehankov?
Jonathan	It's Miss Sheehan's secret Russian name
Louise	Oh, right.
Tricia	Yeah, well she'll give the signal when the train's filled up with us lot, and the man what works the Corkscrew will switch the tracks so instead of goin' back to the beginning, the ground opens up and we go plummeting down into the centre of the Earth.
James	Wicked.
Louise	Yeah, like a roller-coaster in the dark.
James	Mad.
Anna	But won't older people see us go down inside the Earth?
Tricia	No. 'Cos this like-see-urm-this invisibility shield thing gets activated as we get to a certain point on the ride and we go down and no-one sees. It's well advanced.
Tom	Wow. Those Russians are clever.
Hal	Yeah.
Anna	But our parents will notice we've gone.
Tricia	For a while, yeah. But you know all these

kids that vanish like when they're skiin' and stuff?

Louise   Yeah?

Tricia   That's where they've gone. We'll probably see them down there .

Rab   They died didn't they?

Tricia   That's what everyone was told. But it's all part of a 'spirisy.

Anna   Spirisy?

Tricia   That's what it is, a 'spirisy.

James   But how did those skiing kids get down?

Tricia   Similar way. Only the chair-lift things suddenly change course and go down.

Louise   So what they gonna say happened to us?

Tricia   Oh, we'll probably be one of those 'School Bus Off Cliff' tragedies.

You'll see some of the names have changed, more dialogue has been added or reassigned to flesh out some of the characters, sometimes the order has been adjusted. Both versions of the script were workshopped over a period of time with young actors who provided advice on the most up-to-date use of language.

Writing task

1 Draw up a list of slang words that appear in the first and second version of the play. Compare the two lists. Create a slang glossary to accompany the script.

2 Does your school have a different set of words to the ones the children in the play use? The words and sayings in the play will date very fast. Draw up a list of words that would keep the play up-to-date in your school.

HIDDEN WORLDS

Tricia and Ben have the others imagine they can journey to the centre of the earth when the Alton Towers chair lift suddenly changes course:

Ben I think it's very possible that the terrorists could actually be living in the centre of the earth. Tricia's accounts have, in fact, been accurate.

Rab Tricia's whats have been what?

Tricia How would you know? I mean, they have been, but how the hell do you know that?

Ben *(pause)* I've been there.

Tricia Shut up.

Anna How did you get down?

Ben In a chair-lift. Like Tricia said.

What they are describing is a magical means of entering another world. This sits alongside Alice falling down a rabbit hole in Lewis Carol's *Alice In Wonderland,* Will cutting into a parallel universe in Phillip Pullman's *The Subtle Knife* and the following entry from another classic novel.

Read this extract from *The Lion The Witch and The Wardrobe* by C.S. Lewis.

There was nothing Lucy liked so much as the smell and feel of fur. She immediately stepped into the wardrobe and got in amongst the coats and rubbed her face against them, leaving the door open, of course, because she knew that it is very foolish to shut oneself into any wardrobe. Soon she went further in and found that there was a second row of coats hanging up behind the first one. It was almost quite dark in there and she kept her arms stretched out in front of her so as not to bump her face into the back of the wardrobe. She took a step further in – then two or three steps – always expecting to feel woodwork against the tips of her fingers. But she could not feel it.

"This must be a simply enormous wardrobe!" thought Lucy, going further in and pushing the soft folds of the coats aside to make room for her. Then she noticed that there was something crunching under her feet. "I wonder is that more mothballs?" she thought, stooping down to feel it with her hand. But instead of feeling the hard, smooth wood of the floor of the wardrobe, she felt something soft and powdery and extremely cold. "This is very queer," she said, and went on a step further.

Next moment she found that what was rubbing against her face and hands was no longer soft fur but something hard and rough and even prickly. "Why, it is just like branches of trees!" exclaimed Lucy. And then she saw there was a light ahead of her; not a few inches away where the back of the wardrobe ought to have been, but a long way off. Something cold and soft was falling on her. A moment later she found she was standing in the middle of a wood at night-time with snow under her feet and snowflakes falling through the air.

Lucy felt a little frightened, but she felt very inquisitive and excited as well. She looked back over her shoulder and there, between the dark tree-trunks, she could still see the open doorway of the wardrobe and even catch a glimpse of the empty room from which she had set out. (She had, of course, left the door open, for she knew that it is a very silly thing to shut oneself into a wardrobe.) It seemed to be still daylight there. "I can always get back if anything goes wrong," thought Lucy. She began to walk forward, *crunch-crunch* over the snow and through the wood towards the other light. In about ten minutes she reached it and found it was a lamp-post. As she stood looking at it, wondering why there was a lamp-post in the middle of a wood and what to do next, she heard a pitter patter of feet coming towards her.

Writing task

Look at how both Tricia and Ben describe the centre of the earth on pages 50–54. Here they are making it up for the benefit of the other school children. Now imagine they have really gone there. Describe the world they have entered. Write this in the style of a novel – as above.

CONSPIRACY THEORIES

A lot has changed in the world since the first version was written. You'll see that Miss Sheehan has become a terrorist rather than a Russian spy. This is because the more recent dramatic and tragic World events (terrorist bombings and wars) have far outweighed the earlier fall of the Soviet Union in the publics' view.

For every major notable event in history there will usually be several far-fetched conspiracy theories. These theories are often marvellously stupid stories that have sprung from high profile events or situations that contain some element of mystery or coincidence. They generally leap to a wildly improbable conclusion without any real evidence to support it. Tricia has taken a number of real-life events and transposed them into her very own conspiracy (spirisy) theory. She plants the idea Miss Sheehan is up to no good and that they are all in grave danger of being transported to the centre of the earth via a rollercoaster.

"There are too many stories of missing kids who've vanished when skiing and stuff and this will end up as being reported as one of those 'School Bus Off Cliff' tragedies."

She compares this conspiracy with one of the most popular of all time concerning the death of the then Princess of Wales who died in a car accident in a tunnel in Paris in 1997.

Tricia That's what it is. The Spirisy

Anna The Spirisy?

Tricia You know. Like Diana.

Chrissy Who's Diana?

Tricia You know, the princess who was killed by

the Queen. That was the beginning of the Spirisy. The Queen wanted Diana to marry her son but Diana wanted to marry Saddam Bin Laden so the Queen poisoned Diana's driver…

Mathew Oh is that why he knocked down the Twin Towers?

Tricia Yes, because Diana had twins in her tummy when she was killed by the Queen, so Saddam knocked down the Twin Towers to get revenge, then Prime Minister Bush smashed up the Arabists, because he is in love with the Queen who's actually a lizard. That's the Spirisy.

Obviously, Tricia's conspiracy theory is as silly as it's possible to get. She has misheard and misunderstood numerous conversation and news bulletins and pieced them all together in a preposterous way.

However, because conspiracy theories are based on real-life events and people, they can often be upsetting and damaging to those concerned. Much in the same way as irresponsible media coverage can cause distress when facts are distorted.

Writing

Imagine you are a newspaper journalist. Decide whether you are going to cover this school journey incident in a responsible or sensational way. Start with the heading of your article. Would you call it a 'School Bus Off Cliff Tragedy' or something else?